THE
HISTORY
OF THE
WORLD
ACCORDING TO

THE
HISTORY
OF THE
WORLD
ACCORDING TO

50 years of headlines as seen by the 20th century's greatest cartoonist

Written and compiled by John Field

EXPRESS NEWSPAPERS

hamlyn

This book is dedicated to my new grandson, Jacob, and his cousins – Edward, Florence, Millie, Hebe, Cicely, Monty, Sam and Clementine – with the hope that the times through which they live are not quite so tumultuous as those covered in this book.

An Hachette UK Company
www.hachette.co.uk

First published in Great Britain in 2010 by
Hamlyn, a division of Octopus Publishing Group Ltd
Endeavour House
189 Shaftesbury Avenue
London WC2H 8JY
www.octopusbooks.co.uk

Introduction, captions and cartoon selection by John Field

ISBN 978-0-600-62113-3

A CIP catalogue record for this book is available from the British Library

Printed and bound in India by Gopsons Papers Ltd
1 3 5 7 9 10 8 6 4 2

Contents

Introduction

This book covers the history of the world, as depicted by Giles' cartoons, from the end of the Second World War (with a cartoon showing Londoners celebrating the final victory in May 1945) to one of his last cartoons, drawn in 1992, marking the first linking of the Channel Tunnel, which heralded the end of the physical separation of Britain from mainland Europe.

Throughout this period, the world was going through a succession of momentous changes and events, including the 'so-called' Cold War between the then two great world powers – the USSR and the USA – and the Space Race that developed between them; the development of the world's most destructive weapon; and a series of world crises, including Suez and Cuba. In addition, Britain's loss of Empire and influence, entry into Europe and a number of events such as the Profumo Affair, Beeching's 'Axe' and the introduction of the NHS, were all of great national interest. The 150 cartoons chosen for inclusion in this book illustrate many of these world and national events, which occurred over the period of almost five decades during which Giles worked for the Express Group, following the war.

How Giles worked

To decide upon a subject to inspire that day's cartoon, Giles and his wife, Joan, would go through the newspapers each morning, identifying possible news items of interest. On some occasions, there were so many things of importance happening at home and abroad that Giles had difficulty in deciding what to comment upon. This is illustrated by the cartoon that appeared in the *Daily Express* on February 3, 1950, featured opposite, which shows Giles at his drawing board in his home studio (he also had a studio in central Ipswich), with Joan trying to clean up around him. The scene through the window is an accurate representation of the view.

During the previous weekend, US President Harry Truman had announced that he had ordered work to start on the development of the hydrogen bomb. The world's newspapers stated that this bomb would be the world's greatest weapon of mass destruction and "may be more than 1,000 times more destructive than the atom bombs dropped over Japan" at the end of the Second World War.

On the same day, the British Minister of Food, John Strachey, announced various changes to food rationing. These included the ending of price control on rabbits and hares on June 1 and poultry on July 1. Newspaper reports at the time do not reveal any reference to food for pigeons, so this is, almost certainly, Giles in a facetious mood, but at long last things were getting a little better and, by using a slightly ludicrous example, Giles allowed the public to laugh a little at the still very austere situation.

The choice for a cartoon on this occasion, therefore, was between a news item that heralded the fact that the world was soon to have a

"What's it going to be for today – Hydro-Bs or pigeon food?"

weapon so destructive as to bring about its end, and another about a much more insular problem facing the hard-pressed British public at that time.

It has to be noted that Giles did not record every major event of world importance during the 50-year period covered in this book; some, such as Kennedy's assassination, were perhaps considered too sensitive to illustrate in cartoon form. In addition, space does not permit the inclusion of every cartoon of interest here, but this compilation does shed a particular light on this period of recent history, enhanced by Giles' unpredictable brand of humour and insight.

Giles' career

Although his family came from Suffolk, Carl Giles himself was born in Islington, London, on September 29, 1916. Despite no real art training, he started work as an office boy in an advertising agency, but was quickly promoted to the animation studio creating film cartoon movement. After a period with film-maker Alexander Korda, when he worked as an animator on a number of cartoon films, he moved to the Ipswich studio of Roland Davies, where he again worked as a cartoon animator.

Just before the beginning of the Second World War, he went back to London for his first full-time job, as a cartoonist, with Reynolds News. In September 1943, he moved to the Express Newspaper Group, with whom he spent the rest of his cartooning career. On September 19, 1944, he flew into Belgium as the Group's cartooning war correspondent and remained with the troops, as they fought their way across northern Europe, until the last days of the war.

He married his cousin, Joan, on March 14, 1942, at St John's Church in East Finchley and they began their married life in a rented cottage just outside Ipswich. In 1946, they moved to Hillbrow Farm, near Witnesham, some 6.5 km (4 miles) from the town, where they remained for the rest of their lives. Giles died on August 7, 1995, seven months after Joan.

In total, Giles produced three or four cartoons a week for the Express Group for 50 years. He quickly achieved national recognition, and in 1959 was awarded an OBE for his contribution to the cartoon world. In 1962, he received a special award for 'Distinguished Services to Cartooning' from the Cartoonists' Club of Great Britain, and in the 1970s he was made President of the British Cartoonists' Association. He was awarded Senior Fellowship of the Royal College of Art in 1990, and in April 2000, five years after his death, he was voted 'Britain's favourite cartoonist of the twentieth century'. In 2005, the Press Gazette chose him as one of the 40 journalists to be included in its Newspapers Hall of Fame.

In order to illustrate the high opinion in which Giles and his work were held by the nation, a number of extracts from the forewords of various Christmas Annuals, written by celebrities and figures of national importance, are included in Chapter One. These leave no doubt as to the extent to which Carl Giles became a well-loved and nationally important figure.

Chapter One
The Christmas Annual Forewords

"The funniest cartoonist in the world" (Tommy Cooper)

From early on in his cartooning career, Carl Giles' work became so highly regarded nationally that it took him to the highest circles in British society. Royalty, politicians, entertainers and many other well-known personalities in Britain all knew of him, and most, if not all, greatly admired his work. This prominence led him to friendships with many well-known figures.

This chapter demonstrates Giles' national and international appeal by looking at some of the forewords that appeared in each of the Annuals, which were for many years, and still are, regular Christmas gifts in many British homes.

The broad appeal of Giles' work was such that even members of the Royal Family were prepared to give it a 'royal seal of approval' by providing forewords for publications relating to his cartoons. As shown later in this chapter, Prince Charles provided a very warm and personal tribute for the first Christmas Annual to be produced after Giles' death in August 1995, and his father, the Duke of Edinburgh, was pleased to contribute an equally appreciative foreword for Peter Tory's book *The Ultimate Giles*, also published in that year, in which **Prince Philip** wrote,

"Giles combined a great talent for draughtsmanship with a highly developed sense of humour. Whatever the message he wished to convey, his cartoons were, above all, funny. He had a genius for pulling people's legs without being cruel or offensive. I say this as one who has been the subject of several of his efforts and I don't think I would have been unhappy to hang the original of any of his cartoons in my collections."

Peter Tory has recorded that Prince Philip has no fewer than fifteen Giles originals in his personal collection.

A wide range of well-known and important national, and some international, figures have also been pleased to provide forewords for the Christmas Annuals, illustrating the high degree of Giles' fame throughout the country and beyond. These people were, primarily, from the entertainment world and the media, and the following extracts throw a strong light upon the character and various skills of the man himself.

In the first few years of the publication of the Giles Christmas Annuals, immediately following the end of the Second World War, the forewords were provided by people involved in one way or another with the Express newspaper group itself. For example, that which appeared in the 6th Annual (1951–2) was written by **Osbert Lancaster**, a fellow cartoonist at the *Daily Express*. He said,

"The work of Giles, like that of all great artists, has many aspects. There is Giles the nature-lover whose cows have frequently, and most favourably, been compared to those of Cuyp. Giles the landscapist who lives in the Constable country and carries on the best traditions of Gainsborough in that painter's birthplace. There is Giles the recorder of intimate domestic interiors who combines the scrupulous fidelity of a Vermeer with the warm affection of a Chardin."

In the following year, the proprietor of Express newspapers, and the man responsible for enticing Giles away from Reynolds News to work for the Express, **Lord Beaverbrook**, wrote in the foreword for the 7th Annual (1952–3),

"Giles has an immense following. His cartoons give immense joy to millions of Express readers. They are extensively reproduced in the United States and syndicated in the British Empire. They brighten the pages of newspapers at home and abroad. The demand for them is insatiable. What is the secret? It is this: Giles has a sardonic humour, which appeals because he always keeps close to the street and the farm. He depicts the attitudes of ordinary people.

Ordinary people habitually make caustic comments about high-flown pretensions. They are delighted when such comments are made by a man of genius. Giles debunks the vainglorious. He takes the solemnity out of the grand occasion. He helps the world to keep sane by laughing at its soaring moments."

No doubt, as a good businessman, Lord Beaverbrook's admiration for Giles' work was also based a little upon the added value the regular appearances of the cartoons gave to his newspapers' circulation figures.

In a different area of our national life, equal praise for Giles' work was provided by the artist **Pietro Annigoni**, who is perhaps most well known for his famous portrait of the Queen. In the 10th Annual (1955–6), Annigoni wrote,

"He is wonderful, your Giles. I saw him first four years ago, when I arrived in England. I always look for his cartoons. We now have them reprinted in Italian papers. He is very popular there."

Giles's cartoons were even being enjoyed in Italy!

As will be obvious from some of the following quotations, Giles' humour and skills were greatly admired by the most well-known people in the British entertainment and theatre world. In the 12th Annual (1957–8), **Gilbert Harding** (journalist and radio and television personality) said,

"It is Giles's acute contemporary observation that is outstanding. He has genuine wit without malice that makes most of us his debtors. He draws with a chuckle, not with a snarl."

Two of the nation's most well-loved radio and theatre entertainers from the comedy world at that time also paid their tributes in forewords. The first, **Bud Flanagan**, was making our country laugh both before and throughout the Second World War. In the 15th Annual (1960–1), he wrote,

"It is very seldom that a verbal comedian can pay tribute to a comedian in a rather more difficult field. Never in the history of Journalism, in my opinion, has there been as great a cartoonist as Giles", adding, *"In these times of crisis, there is nothing in my opinion more suitable for a Christmas present than a good laugh. It is just as good as a bottle of medicine. For a tonic I recommend the Giles Christmas Book."*

The second, **Spike Milligan**, best known, perhaps, for his role in the *Goon Show*, wrote in the foreword to the 17th Annual (1962–3),

"I can't compete with the devastating humour he produces, which embraces all stratas of life, and makes them hilarious" and *"During the war his cartoons (drawn under active service conditions) played no little part in boosting my morale."*

From the world of classical music, **Sir Malcolm Sargent**, the famous conductor, particularly well-known for being the Chief Conductor of the Summer Proms in the Royal Albert Hall in 1948–67, provided the foreword for the 18th Annual (1963–4). He said,

"To mix a metaphor, he always seems able to 'leg-pull' by 'hitting the nail on the head' – a noteworthy achievement. When this is combined with an exceptional craftsmanship in drawing, we are face to face with something approaching Genius."

Jim Clark (the dominant Formula One racing car driver of his era, winning two World Championships in 1963 and 1965), provided the foreword for the 19th Annual (1964–5), in which he said,

"Giles has been my favourite cartoonist for as long as I can remember. It wasn't only his superb drawings and splendid characters that first attracted me, it was the wonderfully accurate and almost affectionate way he drew cars into his cartoons.... Not everyone realised just how much of a motoring enthusiast Giles really is. His enthusiasm has been recognised by the British Racing Drivers' Club – the club that every young race driver would like to join. He was made an honorary member in November 1961."

The glamorous world of the silver screen produced two more famous fans. **Sean Connery** (actor and star of the early Bond films) wrote in his foreword for the 20th Annual (1965–6),

"The Giles annual is always a marvellous yearly backlog of what we have all been through and how absurd, mad, sad, ridiculous and funny, life, politics, religion and the world is. This year is my turn to thank him."

Three years later, **Richard Attenborough**, the well-known film actor and producer, wrote in the 23rd Annual (1968–9),

"I am profoundly grateful to have been given the opportunity to say – Thank you, Giles, for the countless moments of pure joy you have given not only to me but to millions and millions of others."

The media world provided the foreword for the 27th Annual (1972–3), with **Michael Parkinson** (British broadcaster and journalist) saying,

"His humour is never hurtful or vicious. It touches all of us who are possessed of that most important human quality, the ability to laugh at ourselves. The man who can make us do that is not simply a gifted cartoonist, he is an important part of our lives and therefore he is blessed."

In the early 1970s comedians were the kings of the small screen. Three of the biggest were Giles fans. In the 28th Annual (1973–4), **Mike Yarwood** (impressionist and comedian) said,

"Giles has not only got a wonderful sense of humour, he is also a fine artist. His cartoons are not scribbled, they are carefully constructed. With most cartoonists you get a single laugh out of a cartoon, with Giles you can get as many as a dozen."

A year later, **Tommy Cooper** (comedian and magician) wrote in the 29th Annual (1974–5),

"I think Giles is the funniest cartoonist in the world. He makes me, like millions of others, laugh out loud. He appeals to all ages. His dogs and animals have such funny faces, you can see what they are thinking and are almost human."

In the following year, **Eric Morecambe** (comedian and half of the extremely popular Morecambe and Wise comedy duo) wrote in the 30th Annual (1975–6),

"Every one of his cartoons is like a five-minute television sketch. There is so much to find in the background after you have had your initial laugh at the main joke."

Giles' fame as a cartoonist indeed spread far beyond the shores of this country. From the other side of the Atlantic, **Frank Sinatra**, the famous singer and Hollywood film star, was asked to provide the foreword for the 33rd Annual (1978–9), and he wrote,

"To Carl – who has been so kind to me through the years and who, I believe to be one of the funniest men in the world – Francis Albert."

The next two forewords were written by men from the world of television. In the 34th Annual (1979–80), **Dennis Norden** (comedy writer and television presenter) wrote,

"Breakfast is reckoned to be a highly important meal, if only because many wives get upset if you're not home by then. For me, however, it comes at a time of day when my bio-rhythms are giving a practically nil reading. That's why the only thing I would ever be prepared to say in its favour is that it brings the daily Giles cartoon. Over the years, his squat and malignant creatures have done more to equip me for the day that lies ahead than any of the highly touted mixtures of wheat-chaff and bran."

In the 36th Annual (1981–2), **Terry Wogan**, another very well-known television presenter, said,

"In the course of this fateful evening (at the Saints and Sinners Dinner), in a moment of weakness, Giles asked me to write this introduction. He regrets it now, of course, but it is too late. Like the rest of you, I've admired the man's brilliance for too long to let an opportunity like this go by. There's more going on in a darkened corner of a Giles cartoon than most other artists achieve in a lifetime."

In the 40th Annual (1985–6), **Bobby Robson** (England football manager) declared,

"The first requirement for survival as a football manager is undoubtedly a sense of humour. In a profession where the one sure thing is the applicability of Murphy's Law that whatever can go wrong will, he who laughs not lasts not. The ability to extract humour from uncompromising situations is priceless and, as far as I am concerned, there is no-one in the world better at this than Giles. His characters are fallible and prone to error – just like footballers (and their managers)."

British actress and film star **Joan Collins** provided the foreword for the 41st Annual (1986–7), saying,

"A Giles cartoon isn't like any other cartoon. It is deeply detailed with subtly hidden humours lurking in every corner. It is indeed a veritable gem to study and laugh at with the morning tea."

Another British actress and television star, the well-known **Joanna Lumley**, wrote for the 47th Annual (1992–3),

"From Giles' backdrops I have developed a passion for his England in summertime: hot empty urban streets shadowed by wonderfully drawn trees; sodden cricket pitches, fly-ridden picnics and seedy boarding houses. Giles draws winters like no-one else, thick snow settling on ledges and railways, dark skies over rain-lashed harbours and empty railway stations, Whitehall in a blizzard. Hordes of people have come to life through Giles' pen, each one a complete individual drawn with acute observation. Distant figures are treated in extravagant detail, and all his pictures reward close scrutiny."

Prince Charles was asked to provide the foreword for the 50th Annual (1995–6) – the first Christmas Annual to appear after Giles' death. (The high regard in which Giles was held by members of the Royal family is perhaps best illustrated by the fact that when Prince Charles and Princess Anne gave a dinner in honour of their parents' silver wedding anniversary, back in November 1972, they asked Giles to provide a cartoon to illustrate the cover of the dinner programme.) For his foreword, the Prince wrote,

"For countless people who, like myself, have grown up in Britain since the Second World War, "Giles" has been a much loved "institution". I myself always looked forward to his cartoons. Somehow they captured almost unerringly the mood of the nation. His gently wicked, yet never vindictive, humour, wherever it was applied – to politics, my family, the day-to-day incidents and dramas of life in Britain and abroad – endeared him to all of us in a way that no other cartoonist has achieved this century ... Carl Giles will be missed by many people, both in Britain and overseas, but his ability to distil and to civilise the essence of our world with his humour will live on."

The foreword for the 54th Annual (1999–2000) was by **Dame Thora Hird** (actress), who wrote,

"Someone once said 'Take your work very seriously and yourself not at all'. They were wise words and ones I have tried to follow throughout my career in the theatre – they always come back to me whenever I open a new Giles Annual. Giles took his work very seriously and the world he created laughed all traces of our famous British self-importance out of the window! You know what I love about a Giles cartoon is it's richness. There is so much going on! Once you have laughed at the main punchline –

always so witty and cleverly observed – there are all the other hilarious things in the background."

Another indication of the geographical spread of Giles' fame is provided in the foreword to the 55th Annual (2000–01). Written by **Sir Trevor McDonald**, who became very well-known and popular with the British public as a TV newsreader and journalist, it says,

"I became a fan when I was relatively young and living in Trinidad in the West Indies. Under the influence of my father who had little time for reading too many books, we were encouraged as a family to join in the fun of looking at Giles cartoons because they brilliantly encapsulated almost every aspect of life and with great wit, verve, bite and humour."

The Pig-breeder – we're not particularly interested in because we think that to be a successful farmer you have to be a full-time farmer and nothing else.

The Car Enthusiast – we do NOT love. I boycott all meetings where he is racing and show complete indifference whether he wins or loses – a campaign which I know will slowly but surely bring about the divorce of Husband Number Five from the rest of us."

She added, regarding Lord Beaverbrook's comments on Giles (see page 11),

"[the] remark by Lord Beaverbrook (regarding caustic comments) I wholeheartedly endorse. Anybody who wants to hear some real caustic comment on highflown pretensions and everything else should be around our house at breakfast time and listen to the 'man of genius' going through the morning papers."

Finally, she revealed that,

"All my husbands, like all husbands, have one thing in common – fairly regular lapses into vagrancy."

The last words in this chapter have been left to Giles' wife **Joan**, who, of course, knew him better than anyone else. In the foreword to the 8th Annual (1953–4), she said (in précis form)

"I have at least five husbands. All equally unpredictable. All never quite get-at-able. All under the same marriage licence. They are,

The Cartoonist – we love because he and his drawings make us laugh.

The Engineer – we love because in the monster mobile studio he designed and built himself he gave so much thought and space to all the very mod. con. kitchen – even if it was as much in his own interest as mine.

The Designer and Builder – we love because he converted a gloomy junk-box of a farmhouse into a really livable and cheerful house.

Chapter Two
1945–1949

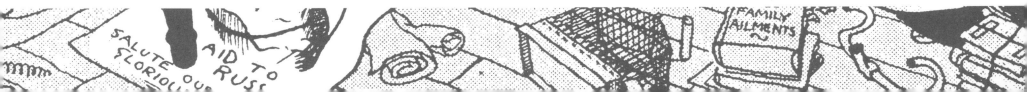

Victory celebrations 1945

On August 15, 1945, after almost six years of military conflict, which covered a large part of the globe and resulted in the deaths of many millions of people, the final step with victory over Japan brought about mass celebrations throughout the country. In this cartoon, Giles captured the widespread and spontaneous outpouring of joy in the nation's capital, where tightly packed crowds milled and danced between Buckingham Palace, Whitehall, Trafalgar Square and Piccadilly Circus.

"Be funny if the siren went now wouldn't it?"

G.I brides

It is estimated that around 45,000 British girls married American servicemen during the Second World War. After the war, the US authorities were keen to get their servicemen home quickly and stated that GI brides may have to wait up to a year before joining their husbands in the States. On October 11, 1945, around 1,000 of them marched to the US Embassy to protest at the delay. The demonstration was successful in that the US authorities relented and the length of their wait was significantly reduced.

"Says he's as much right here as they have – married an American Red Cross nurse or something."

Nuremberg trials

At the Nazi trials in Nuremberg, Goering, who escaped execution by committing suicide the night before, is on the left, next is Hess, who died in Spandau Prison in Berlin in 1987 and then von Ribbentrop, who was hanged for war crimes. Observers at the trials were struck by the apparent ordinariness of such evil men and Giles underlined this by illustrating Hess listening to a popular English comedian of the time whose much-loved weekly programme was on the BBC during the war.

"Sh! Listen! I've got Tommy Handley!"

Food shortages at Christmas 1945

The ending of the war did not bring the end of food shortages – these carried on for many years. By 1948, rationing still covered ham and bacon, cheese, butter, eggs, sugar, tea, milk and sweets. Meat rationing did not finish in Britain until 1954. During the war and after, much food was shipped from the US, and the British public was more used to such things as powdered milk, tinned fruit, dried eggs and, of course, spam rather than what the man in the pub was being offered – hence his reaction.

"All I said was, 'Would you like a nice turkey and a bottle of whisky at controlled price?' and BANG – down he went."

Stafford Cripps with Gandhi in Delhi

Stafford Cripps was in India to discuss with Gandhi the path towards Indian independence, which was achieved just over a year later. On August 14, 1947, Pakistan was declared a separate nation and at midnight on August 15, 1947, India became an independant nation. At the time, Cripps was also responsible for clothes rationing back in Britain. Early in the war clothes rationing was introduced and went on to last until 1949.

Initially each person had 66 points for clothing, which dropped to 48 and then to 36 points. This period of austerity brought about a strong mentality of 'make do and mend', with all sorts of clothing improvisation becoming fashionable. In this cartoon Giles was probably remembering Gandhi's visit to Lancashire in September 1931, when, despite our weather, he travelled dressed basically as illustrated in this cartoon, much to the delight of the ordinary British public, who gave him a warm welcome.

"Before we get down to business, Stafford, I suppose you couldn't let me have a couple of clothing coupons?"

The atom bomb

The addition of the atom bomb to the arsenal of war changed, forever, military and political thinking amongst the world's major powers. These elderly ex-soldiers, however, obviously remained committed to the fighting methods of their youth, when, presumably, the strategy was that you waited until you could see the 'whites of their eyes'. The use of atomic bombs on the Japanese cities of Hiroshima and Nagasaki was followed by a race by various countries to develop ever more powerful weapons.

"Bah! The world's going soft, sir. We managed our wars without atom bombs in my young days."

Soldiers in battle, 1946

Not long after the end of the Second World War, British soldiers found themselves in conflict situations in parts of the world including India and Pakistan. The then Palestine was a British Mandate. During 1946, attacks were made on police stations and military positions, culminating with the bombing of King David Hotel in Jerusalem, location of the British military command, on July 22, 1946. Carried out by a Zionist group, this attack killed 91 people. Britain withdrew from Palestine in May 1948.

"Did you get home at all for the peace celebrations last year Fred?"

Bread rationing

Following the Second World War, the UK went through many years of austerity and experienced an extended period of hardship and shortages, including various types of food and clothes rationing. Starting in July 1946, and lasting for two years, bread rationing was introduced by the Labour Government, causing Churchill to state that it was 'one of the gravest announcements that I have ever heard made in the House (of Commons) in the time of peace'.

Crimes of the times.

British Housewives' League

The British Housewives League was established in 1945 to provide housewives with 'an effective voice in all matters concerning the welfare of themselves and their families'. It quickly acquired a reputation for its forthright views and for taking strong action. The day before, Sir Stafford Cripps stated that there would be great shortages ahead, with the British housewives facing the biggest problems. The RSM here was right to prepare his battle-hardened troops for major troubles ahead.

"You can start thinking of El Alamein, D Day, and the rest of 'em as sports outings –
in future you'll be keeping order at the Housewives' League."

World crisis – Berlin blockade

In March 1948, the communist authorities in East Germany issued orders restricting Western traffic between the American, British and French zones of West Germany and West Berlin, which was also under Western control. All trains and trucks were to be searched by the Soviets before they could travel. This was considered to be a manoevre to force the Western powers to allow the Soviet zone to start supplying West Berlin with all the necessary supplies and to be a Soviet move aimed at getting the Western powers out of Berlin altogether. Consequently, the crisis escalated with the introduction of the Berlin Airlift in June and this continued until the following year. It is estimated that the United States Air Force, the Royal Airforce and other Commonwealth nations flew over 200,000 flights during that period. Giles pointed out that, fortunately, the British public still enjoyed their traditional pursuits even in such a period of world tension.

"World crisis or no world crisis they'll turn up on Monday and ride their little 'orses and go up and down and round and round and be 'appy as ...."

Toni and Italian politics

The Italian elections, which took place on April 18, 1948, were subject to extreme verbal aggression and fanaticism on both the left and right sides of the country's politics and were played out against the background of the Cold War confrontation between the Soviet Union and the United States. These elections took place two months after the communist coup in Czechoslovakia. The election was won by the Christian Democrats, which indicated, perhaps, that Toni's politics leaned towards the left.

"Toni, whatever your personal opinions of the Italian election results, let's not be discussing them now."

London Olympics

The 1948 London Olympics were amongst the first international sporting events held after the Second World War. Lord Burghley welcomed the athletes by saying 'the Olympics represented a warm flame of hope for a better understanding in the world which has burned so low'. Dramatic events occurred when the first man to enter the stadium in the marathon, Gailly (Belgium), fell twice during the final lap and finished third, being overtaken by Cabrera (Argentina), gold medal, and Richards (Britain), silver.

"Let's have it again, bud – not enough agony for a winner".

US forces return to UK

In 1948, tensions were mounting in the Cold War, with the Soviets beginning the Blockade of Berlin in April and the West countering with the Berlin Airlift in June. To help both with the airlift and to demonstrate the strength of Anglo-American resolve, the US Air Force returned to Britain in August. Against this background of increasing tension between the two world powers, London's taxi drivers saw a silver-lining – remembering, perhaps, the generosity of the war-time US servicemen.

"Happy days are here again."

Ground nut scheme

In 1948, Britain was still living through a period of severe food rationing following the Second World War. Faced with a significant shortage of cooking oils at home, the government undertook an ambitious scheme to grow ground nuts in (then) Tanganyika. A major problem was the lack of heavy equipment for clearing the jungle and so machinery was brought in from Canada and the Philippines, including Shervicks – part Sherman tank and part tractor. Unfortunately, these failed to do the job adequately.

Several of the other other problems encountered were the fact that the ground was clay-like, making harvesting of the nuts impossible once the rainy season was finished, the fact that many of the trees harboured bees so vicious that bulldozer drivers had to be hospitalized if stung and, as one observer noted, 'In patches the thickets of scrub are impenetrable – a rhinoceros can force a way through, a snake can wriggle through: but no size or shape of animal in between'. The scheme was eventually abandoned in 1951 at a vast loss.

"Letter here from a lady in Cheltenham – says in view of the fact that we're spending £25,000,000 of her taxes can we let her have a few nuts for her cake."

French meat – luxury goods

The French government, concerned about the poor balance of payment situation between the franc and pound sterling, decided to try to improve matters by increasing their luxury goods exports to the UK. As part of the deal, however, they also agreed to export more of their traditional goods, including, 'in the short term', quantities of meat, which was much needed in Britain, where strict meat rationing was still in place and would be so for a further five years.

"It's like this, Lady – the French are sending us a certain quantity of meat providing we buy some of their luxury goods."

United for victory

Less than four years earlier, the Allies were celebrating victory over evil and, no doubt, most people were hoping for a long period of world peace. At the time this cartoon appeared, however, intense fighting in China saw the Nationalists withdrawing to Taiwan, with the communists establishing the government on the mainland. In addition, the previous few months saw a significant intensification of the Cold War in Europe, with major tensions building up between the former Allies.

"Oh dear – why do people tuck so many things away in the attic and forget all about them?"

Daily Express, February 9, 1949   33

World Bank – financial support for Britain

At this time, the economic situation in Britain and in much of war-torn Europe was extremely difficult. Britain was experiencing severe financial problems, particularly with balance of payments. Sir Stafford Cripps and Ernest Bevin were in New York to make the case for substantial financial assistance at the International Bank for Reconstruction and Development. After the conference, Cripps stated that 'the talks had brought Britain's reserve position into a manageable condition'.

"Staff – considering that we have just saved the country from financial ruin, do you think Clem. would mind if we stayed in an hotel tonight?"

Chapter Three
1950–1959

UNO's 5th birthday party

At the Yalta Conference in February 1945, Roosevelt, Churchill and Stalin – the 'Big Three' resolved to establish the United Nations and the conference founding the organization began in April 1945, in San Francisco. It replaced the earlier League of Nations and its aims are to stop wars between countries and to provide a platform for dialogue. With all of the world crises and conflicts going on at this time, one wonders what they were celebrating – unless the fact that the United Nations Organization had survived for five years was, itself, considered to be a success.

"What a dirty trick – some of these flashlights are hand-grenades."

Stone of Scone

The Stone of Scone was taken from Scotland to Westminster Abbey by Edward I in 1296 as a spoil of war and used for almost every coronation at the Abbey since. On Christmas Day 1950, four Scottish students took the Stone from the Abbey and left it at Arbroath Abbey. The police were informed on April 11, 1951; it was retrieved and returned to London, where it remained until 1996, when it went back to Scotland to be kept at Edinburgh Castle. It will be returned to London for future coronations.

"When you've finished swearing at me about your blessed Stone I'll tell you I happen to be a Welshman."

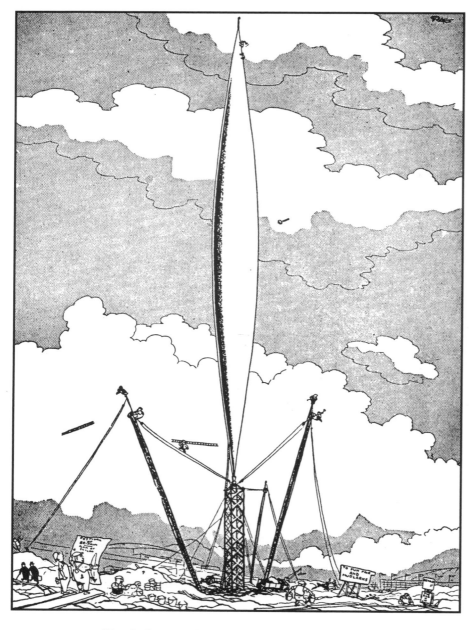

"Handy time to tell us we've built it upside down."

Festival of Britain

The Festival of Britain opened in May 1951 on the South Bank, London. It celebrated the centenary of the 1851 Great Exhibition and, with much of London still in ruins, was designed to give the country a much-needed feeling of recovery. It also aimed to set high design standards for future developments. The Skylon was an iconic feature of the Festival, being a slender, vertical structure, and gave rise to the popular joke that, like the British economy, 'it had no visible means of support'.

Turpin-Robinson fight

On July 10, 1951, the then little-known British boxer Randolph Turpin beat the American fighter Sugar Ray Robinson, much to the delight of the British public. Robinson had lost only one fight in his previous 131, and the Turpin fight went to 15 rounds. Unfortunately, Turpin lost in a return fight, only 64 days later. After much fighting, the war in Korea had reached a stalemate and, also on 10 July, protracted armistice negotiations began, though early hopes for peace were to be frustrated. This vicar's obvious desire to install hopes for peace and the end of violence was being frustrated by both his parishioners and the wider world.

"Miss Edith, do you think we could have less Randolph Turpin and more concentration on our Festival theme?"

Persia nationalizes Anglo-American oilfields

From 1913 the Iranian oil industry was controlled by the British government but in March 1951, Iranian Prime Minister Mosaddeq and the Iranian government decided to nationalize foreign-owned oil fields, which led to a major crisis in the region and caused fears of oil shortages in Britain. The decision to nationalize was seen by many in Britain as an unacceptable breach of contract, and its implementation caused many problems for the country over a long period of time.

"He was a keen little lad – a bit Leftish perhaps – said he wasn't ALWAYS going to work for me.
Been reading the papers a lot lately and this morning he disappeared. So did my oil and pumps."

Change in divorce laws

Although divorce law was to remain related to the irretrievable breakdown of a marriage, the government was considering more liberal laws, which, if enacted, would lead to a situation where, should things go wrong, it would be relatively easy to end a marriage. However, Giles was almost certainly making the point that the changes brought about by this new legislation were not the best basis on which to contemplate getting married.

"Don't worry, son – when she reads how easy they're going to make it to get a divorce she'll change her mind and marry you after all."

Korea – anniversary of peace talks

The Korean War began on June 25, 1950 and finished on July 28, 1953. On one side, South Korea was supported by soldiers from 16 other nations, and on the other, North Korea was joined by Chinese and Soviet troops. Although the war saw a great deal of intense fighting, much of the conflict was spent in a state of stalemate with peace negotiations underway. Giles stressed here the lengthy and difficult negotiations that preceded the eventual armistice, which took another 12 months to achieve. The soldiers participating in this event no doubt hoped that there would be no further such anniversaries to celebrate, only to be disappointed.

"There will be two minutes' silence while this delegation proceeds to the Peace Council to sing 'Happy birthday to you'."

Atom bomb tests in Australia

Following in the steps of the United States and the USSR, Britain, on October 3, 1952, tested its first atomic bomb close to the Monte Bello Islands off the north-west coast of Australia. Code-named 'Operation Hurricane', the bomb was exploded inside the hull of *HMS Plym*, a River class frigate moored around 350 miles from the coast. Although the authorities stated that they were very pleased with the success of the tests, Giles obviously felt that this view was not universal.

"These whites'd probably fine you ten bob if you let a firework off in Regent's Park."

Churchill-Eisenhower meeting

Following the Second World War, Winston Churchill commanded great respect around the world. On a visit to the US in January 1953, Churchill had a much-publicized meeting with Dwight Eisenhower at which Eisenhower tried to persuade him to encourage the UK to take the lead in securing greater European unity, but Churchill resisted this. On the other hand, Eisenhower resisted Churchill's request for stronger Anglo-American ties, believing that the international situation did not warrant it.

"This Churchill-Eisenhower meeting had better come to something – we've had a big run on 'Winstons' and 'Dwights' lately."

Visitors for the Coronation

Queen Elizabeth II was crowned as Monarch on June 2, 1953, at Westminster Abbey, in the presence of more than 8,000 invited guests. These guests included representatives of over 50 member States of the Commonwealth, with 16 being independent states of which she is also monarch. As to be expected with so many visitors staying in London, both from the UK and abroad, good accommodation was very scarce. It is likely that these visitors were expecting something a little more suitable.

"'Enrietta! You know that advert you put in the local paper – 'Coronation visitors catered for'?"

Welsh Eisteddfod

The National Eisteddfod of Wales is a major festival of music, poetry and literature to celebrate Welsh culture. Originally dating from the 12th century, it was revised to its present form in 1860 and since 1880 it has been held every year except 1914 and 1940. If the main aims of the festival include both encouraging greater love of national culture and promoting improved international understanding between different peoples, then this choir leader's approach did not quite capture the spirit of the event.

"To the stage, lads – and sorry I am if we do not bash the living daylights out of our opponents with 'Peace, perfect Peace'."

Brabazon aircraft

The Bristol Brabazon aircraft was an extremely large aircraft, designed to fly the Atlantic route, giving passengers a very high level of comfort. It would have provided enclosed sleeping berths for 80 people, a 37-seat cinema, a dining room, a promenade and bar or, alternatively, day seating for 150 people. Construction of the first prototype's fuselage commenced in October 1945 and the plane made its maiden flight in September 1949. Unfortunately, the aircraft proved to be a commercial failure. Work was stopped in February, 1952 and the sole prototype built was broken up for scrap in October 1953, after only a total of 400 hours flying time.

"Tell us, Sidney – where've they buried the rest of it?"

Strike leaves British holiday makers stranded in France

On August 13, 1953, four million French workers decided on a national strike in protest against strong austerity measures being introduced by the French government at a time of financial crisis in the country. The strike lasted 12 days and affected many things, including public transport, bringing the whole of France to a standstill. The British government, in order to help stranded holidaymakers, arranged for them to receive loans of £3 10 shillings per day.

"Here's to the jolly old Government loan – and may the strike go on forever."

McCarthy era

A product of the Cold War between the Eastern and Western blocs was a near hysterical fear in the United States about the perceived infiltration of communist sympathisers into the fabric of American society. The chief protagonist was Senator McCarthy, who undertook a particularly aggressive investigation into US army personnel, hence this soldier's concern at finding out about the communistic tendencies of his British bride's aunt. McCarthyism has been called 'the politically motivated practise of making accusations of disloyalty, subversion or treason' without proper evidence.

"Honey – this is a swell time to tell me that one of your aunties is a Commie."

Hydrogen bomb

In March 1954, the US carried out Operation Castle Bravo, which tested the world's first hydrogen bomb and created the biggest ever man-made explosion at that time. The test was carried out at the Bikini Atoll in the Pacific and was 1,000 times more powerful than the atom bomb dropped on Hiroshima. The operation prompted calls around the world for the banning of atmospheric testing of thermo-nuclear devices. The test caused considerable concern around the world and newspapers at the time reported that 'the US authorities have admitted that the powers of the Bikini bomb...was far greater than predicted expectations'.

"Great joy was felt by everyone on the Moon when a Moon Air Force squadron reported that the way the Earth-men were carrying on the danger of a visit by Earth Space-ships no longer existed."

Exchanging spies

Part of the 'fun' of the Cold War, at its most extreme, was the exchange of spies, or possible spies, from one side to the other. Sometimes this was a tit-for-tat procedure; other times it was deadly serious. The previous weekend to this cartoon, the British authorities had requested that Moscow should remove two Assistant Military Air Attachés from the Soviet Embassy in London. The two men were suspected of spying. Newspapers reported that no retaliatory action was expected from Moscow.

"Never seem to run into such a thing as a BEAUTIFUL spy these days."

End of rationing

Rationing of many goods was introduced during the Second World War and was part of British life for years after the end of the war. Gradually, however, various items became more available and rationing began to disappear. Sweet rationing ended in February 1953, sugar rationing the following September and, finally, meat rationing ended on July 4, 1954. Obviously this was a sufficiently important day for the nation for Giles to decide to mark it with this cartoon.

"I'm not hungry."

Highland Games v. Farnborough Air Show

The Highland Games in 1954 coincided with the Farnborough Air Show. The Games combine sport with piping and Highland dancing. Farnborough, one of the world's most important air events displaying, both on the ground and in the air, a wide range of British and other military aircraft, was a strong draw. It is clear that, to the boy, the traditional attractions of the event taking place north of the border did not compete at all with the exciting and noisy activities taking place further south.

"I want to go to Farnborough Air Show!"

England slaughtered by Australia

The first test match of the 1954 Series was held at Brisbane, and Australia thrashed England, getting 601 for 8 in their first innings. England could only respond with a first innings of 109 for 10, and 257 for 10 in the second. It is to be hoped, however, that this elderly man survived this early and ignoble defeat, as England went on to win the Series 3–1. Even it being Churchill's birthday could not sweeten his sense of outrage. The next series in 1956 saw England again beating Australia 2–1.

"Martha! Will you kindly refrain from chirping 'Hush dear, it's Churchill's birthday'?"

Daily Express, November 30, 1954

Britain to develop hydrogen bomb

Parliament announced that Great Britain was to proceed with the development of the hydrogen bomb. It was stated by the government that the US was proceeding with the production of such weapons and that the Soviets were following the same policy, and, therefore, the UK should do the same. Giles' cartoon seems to suggest the futility of the whole thing. Britain's first hydrogen bomb was exploded on May 15, 1957, at Christmas Island in the Pacific.

"Warms the cockles of your 'eart, don't it? Now we can all bomb one another."

Russian inspection of British forces

This was a slight exaggeration of the situation by Giles. At the Geneva Summit meeting of the US President, British Prime Minister and Soviet and French Premiers in July 1955, the agenda included discussions on the future of the divided Germany and arms controls. It soon became obvious that agreement would not be reached either on Germany or on arms controls. Eisenhower then dramatically introduced the concept of what became known as the 'Open Skies' proposal. This would have required the US and the USSR to exchange maps showing the location of every military installation in their respective countries. It was recorded later that Eisenhower knew that the Soviets would not accept the proposals but their rejection of the concept would make the Russians look like they were the impediment to an arms control agreement. Some time after the Soviet dismissal of the 'Open Skies' idea, the Eisenhower government approved the use of high-altitude planes (the U2s) for spying on the Soviet Union.

"Many more of these short-notice inspections by the Russians and they'll start a cold war all over again."

Canberra aircraft

On August 23, 1955, a Royal Air Force Canberra jet aircraft completed a round-trip trans-Atlantic flight of 6,920 miles in 14 hours, 21 minutes. This time included a 35-minute stop at Floyd Bennett Airfield, New York, for refuelling and created a record for such a journey. This was the city's first municipal airfield, located in Brooklyn. The merry group shown in this cartoon were, perhaps, a little over-enthusiastic in anticipating their future travelling opportunities.

"The future of Breakfast in London, Lunch in New York, Tea in London, depends on what sort of lunch you have in New York."

Foreign Office – internal security

The day before, the government had decided that the situation in Cyprus was such that it required 'concerted action by all security forces on the island to maintain law and order' and concluded that the British Governor post on the island should be occupied by a high-ranking service officer rather than a diplomat. It was also stated that the island would have a Deputy Governor whose duty would be to assist the Governor in normal work unconnected with security measures.

"Look here, Sanders – are you watching me or am I watching you?"

East-West co-existence

Early in June 1956, the US commenced reconnaissance aircraft flights over Russian soil. On June 24, the Soviets invited foreign delegations from 28 countries to an air show near Moscow. Seven new jet fighter models were displayed. It is likely that the Soviets wished to display that they had weaponry capable of combating any intruders. The event took place at Tushino airfield in the Moscow area and the demonstration greatly impressed the visiting foreign military personnel. In a speech, given a few days earlier, Eisenhower had opened the door to greater co-existence between the West and East power zones.

"O.K., MacElroy – let's not get too many jumps ahead with this co-existence."

Suez crisis

In July 1956, President Nasser of Egypt announced that he was nationalizing the Suez Canal and this was followed by a period of intense political activity, which culminated in Britain, France and Israel attacking Egypt. The military attack on Egypt began on October 31, 1956 with a bombing campaign and President Nasser responded by sinking all of 40 ships using the Canal at the time. This caused the closure of the Canal to further shipping until early 1957. Britain was particularly agitated because of the importance of the Canal to its economic and military interests both in the region and further afield. The soldier here was one of those caught up in this crisis, although it appears that he may have had a crisis of his own.

"I hope he gets a move on – the Town kick-off at two-thirty and my ship sails at six."

Sunday Express, August 19, 1956

Stirling Moss

Egypt's closure of the Suez Canal in November 1956 resulted in a long ocean detour for shipping via the Cape of Good Hope, which continued until the Canal's reopening the following April. At this period, Stirling Moss, the well-known British racing driver, was in the middle of his very successful motor racing career. The previous year he had won the Italian Mille Miglia road race in 10 hours, 7 minutes – a record time – with Moss having covered the 992 miles at an average speed of 99 mph. The Suez Canal, built during 1859–69, is a little more than 160 km (100 miles) in length. It links Port Said on the Mediterranean with the Gulf of Suez, through to the Red Sea and on to the Indian sub-continent and the Far East.

"Steward, who's piloting us these extra five thousand miles round the Cape – Stirling Moss?"

British presence in Libya

As tension built up during the weeks prior to the Suez Crisis, British forces in the Mediterranean found themselves involved. The Libyan government declared its support for Egypt and required British forces stationed there to remain in their bases. This cartoon illustrated an group of British servicemen probably in Benghazi (170 miles east of Tubruk – see sign), who did not want to be there. Maybe they were aware that the British government's threatened action in Egypt did not have universal support.

"'Well,' I said, 'I'm fed up and want to go home,' and this sailor said, 'England expects every man to do his duty, chum,' and I said, 'Nelson wasn't always so hot at doing what he was told, chum,' then he flipped me one, then I flipped him one...."

Britain leaving Jordan

This cartoon almost certainly refers to the withdrawal of British troops from Jordan. Britain's participation in the attack on Egypt during the Suez Crisis the previous year caused the Jordanian government to consider ending its long-standing relationship with Britain. Consequently, the Anglo-Jordanian Agreement signed in March 1957 terminated the British financial subsidy to Jordan and required the handing over of British installations to Jordan and the withdrawal of all British troops still in Jordan. Probably, at times like this, many servicemen would take home little souvenirs and presents but this soldier appears to have been a bit over-zealous.

"Now if Private Wilson had referred to his little regulations book he would have observed there are certain items acquired whilst on overseas service which one is not allowed to take back to the United Kingdom."

Britain tests first H bomb

Four days before this cartoon appeared, Britain tested its first hydrogen bomb at Christmas Island in the Pacific. It, and two further bombs dropped over the next five weeks, exploded at a height of about 5.5 km (18,000 feet). The innocent bonfire in the cartoon was ill timed, bearing in mind the concerns of the public during this period. This led to the founding of the Campaign for Nuclear Disarmament the following year, which pressed for the abandonment of Britain's and, ultimately, all nuclear weapons.

"O wretched boy!"

Queen's visit to US

The Queen, with the Duke of Edinburgh, made her first state visit to the US in October 1957. She attended a State Banquet, hosted by President Eisenhower, at the White House in Washington, and this reception at the Waldorf Hotel in New York. Her visit coincided with the 350th anniversary of the establishment of the first permanent English-speaking settlement in North America, at Jamestown, Virginia, where she said that the town was the beginning of a series of British settlements throughout the world.

"Elmer! I don't give a damn how pro-Monarchist you are – take it off and take it back where you rented it at once."

"Be funny if the Moon Men thought she was an Earth Man and made her their ruler."

Russian Sputnik with dog aboard

In October 1957, the USSR successfully launched *Sputnik* – the first man-made object to leave the Earth's atmosphere. On November 3, *Sputnik II* went into space carrying a dog called Laika. In December 1957, the US sent up a rocket carrying a satellite, but this exploded. However, in February 1958, the US successfully launched its first satellite – *Explorer*. This sequence of events announced the beginning of the Space Race between the USSR and the US.

Brussels Expo

The Brussels Expo 58 was the first World Fair to be held after the Second World War. More than 42 million people visited the Fair, which opened with a call from King Baudouin I for 'peace and social and economic progress'.

Giles used this background to illustrate the high degree of competitiveness that had developed between the two then great world powers at all levels of contact. The Fair contained a giant model of a unit cell of an iron crystal, named the 'Atomium', which Giles draws here.

"Well, the Russians gave us a vodka, so the Americans gave us two rye whiskies, so the Russians gave us four vodkas, so the Americans gave us six rye whiskies, so the Russians gave us eight vodkas, so the ..."

Alaska – 49th State

President Eisenhower endorsed the concept of Alaskan statehood for the first time when Congress reconvened in January 1958. Alaska became the 49th State of the US on July 3, 1958. Giles was playing here with the renowned propensity of US servicemen, all over the world, to check out local talent upon arriving at a new location. Alaska's desire to achieve US statehood was helped by the prominence it got during the Second World War and the Cold War when its situation received nationwide attention.

"The one on the right's the doll – the other one's her old man."

America's Cup

The 'America's Cup', a prestigious international yacht race, originated in 1851 when a cup known as the 'Queen's Cup' was provided by the Royal Yacht Squadron. It became known as the 'America's Cup' after the first yacht to win the trophy – the *America*. In 1958, the race took place between *Columbia*, of the New York Yacht Squadron, and *Sceptre* of the Royal Yacht Squadron. The race was staged off Newport, Rhode Island, and consisted of seven races over 8-mile courses; *Columbia* won 4–0. It was said that the British boat lost without putting up much of a fight, 'overwhelmed by the complete package of *Columbia* and her star crew'.

"Which one are you rooting for, Bud?"

Eisenhower visits Scotland

President Dwight Eisenhower stayed as a guest of the Queen at Balmoral Castle in September 1959. Being President of a major world power, particularly during a period of intensive international tension, such visits, no doubt, required considerable security arrangements to be carried out. Presumably bodyguards and other security agents are trained to mingle, unnoticed, in the local scene, but both the FBI and the MI5 may have tried a little too hard on this occasion.

President Ike's F.B.I. and our own Scotland Yard moving unobtrusively among the good people of Deeside making sure everything will be all right for the President's trip to Balmoral.

Chapter Four
1960–1969

Castro and Jamaica

Soon after becoming leader of Cuba, in January 1959, Fidel Castro developed a good relationship with Jamaica, which is only 145 km (90 miles) to the south. Castro quickly expanded his influence in the region by initially nationalizing US-owned refineries, after they refused to process Soviet oil, and then, in October, nearly all other US businesses on the island were expropriated. General concern was being expressed in some quarters about how far Castro intended to go.

"Rodney – have you invited a boat-load of bearded men for lunch?"

Rome Olympics

Giles was probably influenced by the fact that the Rome Olympics used two restored ancient Roman structures for the Games – the Basilica of Maxentius and the Baths of Caracalla. In addition, Coubertin, the founder of the International Olympic Committee, had once said, 'I want Olympism...to don once again the sumptuous toga'. Bringing back lions, though, is perhaps going a bit too far. The Olympics did, in fact, provide a modern element with the Olympic Stadium and Sports Palace.

"Well, they're not down in the official entries list."

Introduction of traffic wardens in London

On this day, traffic wardens started patrolling the streets of London. It is recorded that the first ticket issued was to a doctor who had parked his car outside a West End hotel to attend to a patient who had suffered a heart attack. The ensuing outcry in the press resulted in the ticket being cancelled. Giles went on to develop a dislike of traffic wardens, particularly in Ipswich, where he lived and worked, and he produced a number of cartoons that, generally, did not show them in a good light.

"Nice start, Henry."

UNO meeting in New York

With Krushchev of the USSR, Nasser of Egypt, Tito of Yugoslavia and Castro of Cuba all in town at the same time for the Fifteenth Session of the UN General Assembly, along with many other of the world's leaders, this was bound to be an exciting time for all. Anyone carrying a billboard on the streets of New York during that period was bound to be in for a certain amount of attention, but, obviously, not the sort they were hired to attract. On a more positive note, this General Assembly saw the biggest increase in membership in any one year with the introduction of 17 newly independent states, 16 from Africa. The total today is 192 member states.

"One thing's for sure — I ain't going to be carrying any messages for Joe's Grill next time UNO meets in New York"

Daily Express, September 23, 1960

Queen visits India

In January 1961, the Queen and Prince Philip left Britain for a six-week tour of India, Pakistan and Iran. Like her illustrious ancestor, the first Queen Elizabeth, Elizabeth II and the Prince were, no doubt, accommodated in a wide range of places, including sumptuous Indian palaces, but none as bizarre, perhaps, as Giles suggested here. Of course, some of the many places in England that claim to have provided overnight accommodation for the first Elizabeth may not be totally authentic.

"An enterprising one is our Rhamjah!"

US space capsule back to Earth – chimp aboard

On January 31, 1961, a chimpanzee named Han was sent into space in a US rocket and returned safely a few hours later. He was trained to pull levers, in response to flashing lights, during the flight and carried out several operations as he travelled at 8,050 kmph (5,000 mph) at a height of 250 km (155 miles) above the Earth. The Americans chose a chimpanzee, rather than a dog, like the Russians, because they were considered to be more similar to humans. His success must have given this chimp some ideas.

"Hey, Sarge – ain't that him moving out with your chick?"

US nuclear submarines in Scotland

The first US nuclear submarine (Polaris) arrived at its new base at Holy Loch, Scotland, on March 9, 1961. During the Second World War the loch was used as a R.N. submarine base. America needed a base for its submarines closer to the Soviet Union. In return for this arrangement, the US sold 100 air-launched ballistic missiles to the UK. The base was important to the US because land-based missile silos and air bases are easy to locate and destroy, whereas submarines at sea are not.

"If ye miss and hit one of yon bonnie submarines it'll be bang – goodnight Europe."

Ban the Bomb march in London

The day before this cartoon appeared saw a large demonstration against nuclear weapons take place in London. An estimated crowd of 25,000 assembled in Trafalgar Square where they cheered speeches from Michael Foot, MP, and Canon Collins. From there, they marched to the American Embassy where a sit-down demonstration was staged. During the following four days, 51 men and women appeared at Marlborough Street and Bow Street Courts on various charges of affray.

"You can come out, Oswald – it was only one of those rotters bursting a paper bag."

Russia puts man in space

On April 12, 1961, Russian cosmonaut Yuri Gagarin became the first human to enter outer space and to orbit the Earth. He immediately became famous and received much admiration from around the world for his pioneering tour in space, particularly from young girls. This trip did much to intensify the Space Race with the US. So close had this race become that only 23 days later, on May 5, US astronaut Alan Shepard became the first American to enter space.

"Good night, Elvis Presley, good night, Cliff Richard – come in, Yuri Gagarin."

French troubles over Algeria

In 1961, France was in turmoil over Algeria. The Algerian National Liberation Front had fought for independence from France since 1954. In April, a group of French generals attempted a putsch against the Gaullist government, whose negotiations appeared to be going towards giving freedom to Algeria. This resulted in the army being greatly discredited. Several of the generals involved were eventually imprisoned but were later granted an amnesty. Algeria achieved independence in March 1962.

"Oddly enough, one of the few places we could have gone where they're not having a revolution at the moment is the U.S.S.R."

Daily Express, April 25, 1961

Construction of the Berlin Wall

The Berlin Wall was built by the East Germans to encircle West Berlin during a particularly bleak period of the Cold War. Construction of the wall commenced on August 13, 1961 and, with its completion several months later, Berlin became a divided city for the next 28 years. On the East Berlin side of the high concrete wall was a wide strip of open land, later known as the 'death strip', created by the demolition of many buildings and which contained various hindrances to prevent East Berliners from escaping to West Berlin. Initially, East German troops and workers tore up streets running alongside the border to make them impassable for vehicles and then put up barbed wire entanglements and fences around the outside of the three Western zones and along the 43 km (27 mile) border separating East from West Berlin. Over the next few months the actual concrete wall was built causing many problems for the Germans with families split up and many East Berliners cut off from their jobs in West Berlin. During the 28 year period it has been said that there were around 5,000 successful escapes into West Berlin and estimates of the number of people killed trying to escape range from around 140 to 200.

"Excuse me – I think you've still got one of my chaps over there."

John Glenn orbiting Earth

Two days before this cartoon, Lieutenant Colonel John Glenn became the first American to orbit the Earth. He travelled 130,350 km (81,000 miles), circling the Earth three times, at an average speed of 27, 350 kmph (17,000 mph) before landing safely in the Altantic ocean. This success came as a great relief to the American public and military because, up until then, the Soviets seemed to be winning the Space Race. Messages from the astronaut were transmitted by radio stations and his progress was monitored around the world. The sense of US pride prevailing, as a result of this event, obviously affected these soldiers deeply.

"During last night's celebration of Colonel Glenn's magnificent achievement no fewer than twenty-five men from this outfit signed on for astronautical duties."

Cuban crisis

During October 1962, the '13 days Crisis' occurred when Cuba allowed Soviet missiles to be located on its soil, facing towards the US. It is generally felt that this is the moment when the Cold War came closest to becoming nuclear. Fortunately, agreement for the missiles' removal was reached and, on November 12, the Russian freighter *Kurchatov* left Cuba carrying missiles back to the Soviet Union – its passage being carefully monitored by the US authorities.

"Boarding party reporting back, sir – 'All missiles on this one labelled Made in Pittsburgh, Pennsylvania.'"

Daily Express, November 13, 1962

De Gaulle vetoes the UK entry to European Community

French President de Gaulle had just vetoed Great Britain's entry into the Common Market, arguing that, 'England's situation differs profoundly from those on the continent'. Some observers felt that it was because he considered that the UK was too close to the US and, therefore, feared greater American influence on the future of Europe if Britain entered. The members of this club were taking the strongest action they could to express their views.

"Agreed then – we send a note to de Gaulle telling him if he don't like Britain this club is cancelling its annual day-trip to Boulogne."

Beeching's plans for the railways

The British government commissioned Dr. Beeching to review the future of the country's railways system with the purpose of bringing down the cost of running it. His report, 'The Reshaping of British Railways', was published on March 27, 1963. Commonly called 'Beeching's Axe', the report called for the closure of a considerable part of the railway system and for the introduction of a wide range of changes to the established system, creating much dismay to the general public.

"Dr. Beeching's plan to streamline the railways don't provide separate freight for Lady Ringboan's 'orse."

Christine Keeler

The Keeler affair concerned the fact that she had been friendly at the same time with John Profumo, the British Secretary of State for War, and a Naval Attache at the Russian Embassy in London – a situation considered by the government to be a major security risk. Then, on June 20, the US Defense Secretary expressed concern that some US Air Force personnel may also have met Miss Keeler. President Kennedy arrived in London for an official visit on June 29.

"We won't detain you long, Miss Keeler. Just until all the American V.I.P.s are out of the country"

Queen of Greece booed in London

King Paul I and Queen Frederika of Greece made an official visit to London during July 9–12, 1963. The Queen's strong sense of patriotism and her equally strong anti-communist sentiments were well-known. During her stay in London, she was met with noisy demonstrations at which 94 people were arrested. The government apologized to the Queen, which prompted questions in Parliament as to why this was necessary. Giles anticipated the possible reaction to this incident in the Queen's country.

"I expect our Greek guide's cross with us because of all this booing in London"

Great Train Robbery

On the night of August 7, 1963, the travelling post office train from Glasgow to London was stopped by criminals and a total of £2.3 million stolen. The drama and daring nature of the event captured the public's imagination, with the exploit spawning a number of books, films and even a pop song. Giles linked the robbery to a typically Hollywood scenario of 'redskins' attacking the stagecoach, anticipating the glamour that almost immediately became associated with the exploit. The Post Master General at the time noted that this was the first successful attempt at a robbery in the 150 years of the travelling post office. The police stated that the train was stopped by a fake signal and the driver of the locomotive was then made to move the train forward about 1.6 km (1 mile) to a road bridge (presumably to facilitate getting the cash away by road). All telephone lines in the area had been cut, including a private line running from Lord Rosebery's estate at Mentmore Towers. Newspapers reported that 'shortly after 3.00 am, a group of men, dressed in boiler suits and faces covered with nylon stockings or balaclavas and armed with crowbars, coshes and, it is believed, a gun' waited for their quarry at the bridge. It was further reported that about 20 or 30 men were involved in the robbery and, unfortunately, the locomotive driver was badly hurt in the attack.

"You know you said it was a hundred to one against another raid bang on top of the other one?"

Churchill's death

Churchill died, aged 89, on January 24, 1965. As the great wartime leader of Britain during the Second World War, he earned the love and respect of many people. His funeral was watched on television by millions of people around the world. His coffin was taken first by gun carriage, then by launch up the Thames and finally by train and hearse to Bladon Churchyard, near his family home, Blenheim. The old soldier, with his medals, may have regretted the depth of his feelings the night before.

"Harry – to treating everybody who came in last night with 'I'm sure the Old Warrior would rather we all had a drink instead of shedding tears' there is a small matter of £5.18.9 outstanding."

Space Race continues

The Space Race continued. On March 18, 1965, Russia again beat the US when their man, Aleskei Leonov, became the first man to walk in space. He spent just over ten minutes outside his *Voskhod 2* spacecraft but remained connected to the craft by a tether. On June 3, the Americans responded with their man, Ed White, also performing the feat. Giles allowed his imagination to run riot with this suggestion that the Soviets' next stage in the race would really 'up the pace' and be something quite impressive.

"Mr. President? I guess they've sure set the pace this time."

World Cup stolen

The football World Cup was stolen on March 20, 1966, while on exhibition at Central Hall in Westminster. The cup, made of solid gold, worth around £30,000 at that time, was taken while a church service was taking place elsewhere in the building. A ransom note was received by the Chairman of the Football Association the following Monday but, a week later, a man walking his dog in south-east London found the cup, wrapped in an old newspaper, lying on the ground, and brought it to the police's attention.

"You didn't exactly have to be a Man from U.N.C.L.E. to shift three small screws and a garden shed padlock."

Daily Express, March 22, 1966

British seamen's strike

The British government declared a state of emergency on May 23, 1966, a week after the country's seamen went on strike demanding that their 56-hour week should be reduced to 40 hours. Emergency powers were introduced on May 26, allowing the Royal Navy to take control of the ports, in order to 'protect the vital interests of the nation'. After 44 days the seamen returned to work on the understanding that a committee would review their working arrangements.

"Bon voyage, Mesdames et Messieurs! To ensure a return journey passengers are advised not to leave the ship on arrival at Calais."

England win World Cup

In the summer of 1966, the 8th FIFA World Cup was staged in England. This country was chosen because that year was the centenary of the codification of football in England. The World Cup was won by the home country after beating Germany 4–2, giving England its first and only World Cup win. It is estimated that 98,000 spectators watched the game. Although Grandma is, normally, a very fervent supporter of England, on this occasion she must have fancied Germany's chances.

"I'm afraid the law to allow me to arrest Grandmas who don't pay their bets on England winning has been abolished, Sir."

Royal Navy quitting South Atlantic base

At the Conservative Party Conference at Blackpool that week, the whole future of Britain's role in the world was one of the motions discussed. There was debate about the country's future military presence east of Suez and elsewhere. It was decided that Britain should continue to carry out her defence obligations until such time as the forces of Commonwealth and other free countries were sufficiently developed to provide their own security. As Giles pointed out, this policy was not well-received by some.

"Let no one remind him today is also Nelson's birthday."

British troops leaving Malta

In late January 1967, the Maltese government decided to withdraw Britain's rights on the island because Britain had reduced the number of its troops stationed there by about two-thirds. The Maltese argued that this was against an agreement reached two years earlier, allowing Britain to retain military bases on the island. At the time, British servicemen were spending around £25 million, each year, in Malta, which contributed significantly to the island's financial budget.

"There's your first international repercussion for calling home the troops – Maria says no more tick."

Kosygin's visit to London

Soviet Premier Alexey Kosygin made an eight-day official visit to London in early February 1967. Prime Minister Harold Wilson hoped to use the visit to discuss, with the Russians, steps towards improving the situation regarding the war in Vietnam, but was not successful. Giles' cartoon suggested that some people in Britain, who were brought up in a different world, were still finding it difficult to adjust to the change of regime in Russia, although it had happened some 50 years earlier.

"But Rodney, we do think it will be a splendid gesture to wear it at Mr. Kosygin's luncheon –
we simply said it is a pity it happens to be a uniform of the late Czar's Palace Guard."

Sunday Express, February 5, 1967   97

Grosvenor Square riots

On October 21, 1967, around 100,000 people attended an anti-Vietnam war demonstration in Washington. The next day, as part of demonstrations taking place around the world, violent clashes occured between demonstrators and the police outside the American Embassy in Grosvenor Square, London. It was estimated that around 3,000 demonstrators had assembled in the Square when trouble broke out, resulting in a number of casualties on both sides, as Giles illustrated in this cartoon.

"Right! Two visitors at a time only and kindly remember this is not Grosvenor Square."

Daily Express, October 24, 1967

1968 Winter Olympics

The 1968 Winter Olympics, held at Grenoble, France, were the first Games to be held where the International Olympics Committee allowed East Germany and West Germany to compete as separate countries. Giles anticipated that this could cause problems. In fact, in the women's Luge event, East German teams came 1, 2 and 4 but were disqualified for warming their runners. They immediately claimed that they were the victims of a 'capitalist, revanchist plot'.

A battalion of the British Expeditionary Force left today to join the UNO Peace Force in Grenoble.

Nixon visits the Queen

President and Mrs Nixon were invited to have lunch with the Queen and Prince Phillip during their two-day official visit to London. Unfortunately, this visit coincided with a difficult period on the international front, with a large crowd of demonstrators mounting a noisy protest about the Vietnam War outside Claridges. Giles always seemed to have enjoyed drawing grand ceremonial occasions and all of their elaborate ceremony, but he may have overdone the flags a little on this occasion.

"Now I've seen everything. Powdering their little red noses for colour TV."

First flight of British Concorde

Following an agreement in 1962 between the British and French governments, the Concorde supersonic aircraft was designed and built in both countries. The British prototype made its first flight on April 9, 1969 from Filton, near Bristol, to RAF Fairford in Gloucestershire, over a month after the French prototype's inaugural flight. Almost certainly, Giles was commenting upon the long wait between the original inception of the idea and it finally taking to the air.

"My tortoise has hibernated in that starboard engine for the last six years. Nobody told me the Concorde was going to get off the ground."

Maiden voyage of the QE2

The liner *Queen Elizabeth II* commenced her maiden voyage, from Southampton to New York, on May 2, 1969, taking just over four days and 16 hours. She was taken out of service in November 2008, after sailing more than 9 million km (6 million miles) and crossing the Atlantic 806 times. Her current owners plan to refurbish her as a luxury floating hotel (like her companion ship, *Queen Mary*, now berthed at Long Beach, California) and a use not far removed from Giles' prophecy in this cartoon.

"Poor dears, they don't know that Elmer has plans to buy her for the biggest goddam casino this side of Texas."

Gibraltar – closure of frontier

On June 8, 1969, Franco's Spain closed its land border with Gibraltar. This move followed a period of gradual but steady decline in cross-border relations that had begun 15 years earlier. The closure resulted in Gibraltar being cut off from its hinterland, and some commentators consider that it marked the beginning of an important phase in the consolidation of a separate Gibraltarian identity. For some, everything has a silver lining.

"Ole! Me and you cut off one side of the frontier, your mother and the kids the other."

First man on the Moon

The *Apollo 11* mission was launched on July 16, 1969, and allowed Neil Armstrong and 'Buzz' Aldrin Jnr to become the first men to walk on the Moon. As he stepped onto the moon's surface, Armstrong made the famous comment, 'That's one small step for man, one giant leap for mankind'. After years of trailing behind the Soviet Union at various stages of the Space Race, this was a major success for the US. The lunar module, included in this cartoon, was named 'Eagle'.

"Nice start, fellas."

Chapter Five
1970–1979

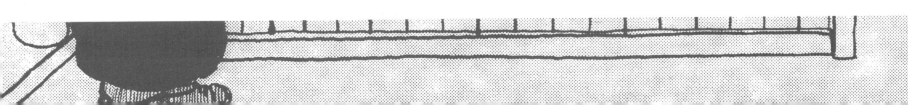

Troubles in Ireland

Northern Ireland was experiencing severe flooding during this period. Under the circumstances, British soldiers, usually the source of resentment among some of the Irish population at that time, were detailed to assist in the rescue operation, and any hostility normally present was temporarily forgotten. 'Any port in a storm', as they say.

"If it isn't the same dharlin' boy I beat the living daylights out of for pinging me one with a rubber bullet!"

Daily Express, August 18, 1970

Hippy Festival – Isle of Wight

Between 1968 and 1970 a large musical festival was held on the Isle of Wight during August. The 1970 festival was the most successful in terms of numbers, with around 700,000 people flocking to the island; however, it was moved to a site with poor access, causing many problems. The day before, Prince Phillip had given a lift to two newly-weds on their honeymoon. The Royal Coach may relate to the Queen and Prince Phillip's habit of watching Cowes Week from HMY *Britannia* moored in the Solent.

"That's great, Ma'am. Thanks for the lift."

Decimal conversion

The Decimal Currency Board anticipated difficulties during the changeover period when Britain went decimal. The Board's chairman stated that, 'it could take months for all cash registers and other machinery to be converted' but added, 'try to think decimal as soon as possible and keep a copy of Shoppers Tables in your pockets'. Decimalization did not come in until February 1, so this publican was also expecting some problems and was setting the ground rules for future transactions in his pub.

"I've been arguing with that one for the last thirty years over £ s.d."

US on Moon

Another major success for the US in the Space Race was the *Apollo 14* mission, which, under the control of Commander Alan Shepard, touched down on the Moon on February 15, 1971 for a nine-day visit. An innovation was the provision of a collapsible two-wheeled cart for carrying tools. The mission collected over 45 kg (100 lb) of moon rock and undertook several surface experiments. Judging from Giles' cartoon, it is surprising that the mission was not charged for the Moon rock which it took back to Earth.

"He says we owe $65.90 on duty. You got $65.90 Ed?"

London Motor Show – foreign cars

Giles was a great lover of cars and had several on the road at any given time. Many of his vehicles, particularly his Land Rover, occasionally appeared in his cartoons. He was also a keen racing car driver, and it is almost certainly the case that he deplored the gradual decline of Britain's motor car industry in the post-war years – a point that comes out very strongly in this cartoon. The 'Buy British' sign is particularly poignant and the marketing aid may have caused some disapproval.

"O.K., luv, Princess Alexandra has gone, but hang on a minute – here come Lord Longford and Malcolm Muggeridge."

Arab-Israeli troubles

In March 1971, a Civil War between West and East Pakistan began, which terminated on December 16, with the independence of East Pakistan under the new name of Bangladesh. A linked 13-day war between India and Pakistan also finished on December 16, with the Indian army having over-run East Pakistan and taken an estimated 93,000 prisoners. It would seem that this school nativity play was very much in line with common occurrences at that time.

"No sooner one war ends than another breaks out – go and tell the producer we've got fresh trouble with Israel and the Arabs."

Staying on in Malta

In January 1972, after several months of dispute, agreement was reached between the Maltese and British governments for Britain to retain bases on the island and for British forces to remain stationed there. No doubt the uncertainty caused by months of indecision resulted in a number of significant complications and domestic problems. On January 14, a BEA Vanguard had arrived at Heathrow Airport with more than 100 dogs, cats and birds on board – all the pets of British service families in Malta.

"Even if your husband did dispose of your cat in undue haste, and assuming we may stay after all,
I doubt if Lord Carrington and Mr. Mintoff can discuss its recovery at the moment."

Malta welcomes tourists

Giles is probably noting here that a few months can sometimes make an amazing difference and little spats between friends can be quickly forgotten – particularly when money is involved. Under an agreement reached on March 26, 1972, the Maltese government granted the UK, 'in peace time and in war the right to station armed forces and associated personnel in Malta and to use facilities there for the defence purposes of the UK and NATO...'.

"Two months ago you set alight to the Union Jack so you go make a new one."

Floating the pound sterling

In June 1972, the British government, faced with major financial difficulties, decided to float sterling, and many countries around the world shifted to the US dollar. At the same time, Britain was experiencing a period of considerable industrial unrest, which led to growing pessimism regarding the future of Britain's balance of payments. All of this was very much to the detriment of the British tourist abroad and the value of the money in his pocket.

"Desmond – before you order another round of Veuve Clicquot-Ponsardin......"

Silver wedding anniversary

Queen Elizabeth and Prince Philip celebrated their silver wedding anniversary on November 20, 1972. Many groups in the country sent them presents, generating, no doubt, many a debate. Prince Charles and Princess Anne decided to give a dinner in honour of the occasion and requested Giles to provide the cover illustration for the dinner programme. He called upon his most loved character, Grandma, and showed her trying to give their Highnesses a nice set of six British Rail spoons.

"I can see 'em now – 'Oo! A little silver gravy boat, just what we wanted'"

Entry into the Common Market

After many years of indecision, debate and a number of rejections, particularly by France, Great Britain finally entered the Common Market at the turn of midnight on December 31, 1972. Public opinion on the move was seriously divided and this uncertainty was evident in the mixed political make-up of the group of MPs who approved of the treaty. It is difficult to decide whether Grandma is jubilant or angered – possibly, with her anarchic and unfathomable character, a little bit of both.

"5...4...3...2...1...Zero!! Pow!! We're in!"

Cod War

The second 'Cod War', between Iceland and the UK, commenced in September 1972, when Iceland extended its limits to 80 km (50 miles). Following attacks on British trawlers by Icelandic fishermen, the government decided that Royal Navy vessels should accompany the trawlers on their fishing trips. They had returned to the task, after a short respite, three days before this cartoon appeared. Agreement was reached in October 1973, allowing the British to fish within certain areas.

"Signal from H.M.S. Jupiter, Sir. 'Landed 10lb Icelandic cod. Frying tonight"

Nixon-Brezhnev in Washington

Soviet leader Brezhnev spent 47 hours in meetings with President Nixon during his six-day stay in America in June 1973. They signed nine accords, including agreements on the Prevention of Nuclear War and on Basic Principles of Negotiations on the Limitations of Strategic Offensive Arms. No doubt this was generally viewed, at the time, as a very welcome softening of the Cold War – Giles suggested that Brezhnev celebrated this by giving Nixon a big Russian bear hug.

"I'll say he was brave to keep smiling through Mr. Brezhnev's visit – that first hug by Honeybear cracked four of his ribs."

Go-ahead for Channel Tunnel

On September 12, 1973, the Government accepted a White Paper that came down in favour of building a rail tunnel between Britain and France, after studies had shown that this was the cheapest way of meeting the rapidly rising demand for Anglo-Continental travel over the next half-century. This decision knocked on the head aspirations, by some people, for a third London Airport at Maplin in Essex, but opened up other possibilities in some people's minds.

"I suppose some of us are already thinking of £468,000,000 in terms of lunchtime trips to the Folies Bergere and back."

Soviet involvement in the Middle East

During October 6–26, 1973, the Israeli-Arab War, also known as the 'Yom Kippur War', between Israel and a coalition of Arab states backing Egypt and Syria, was fought. The conflict began with a surprise attack against Israel by Egypt and Syria on Yom Kippur, the holiest day of the year for religious Jews. The war had far-reaching implications for many nations in the Arab world. On October 9, as the conflict developed, the Soviet Union began airlifting various supplies to Egypt and Syria. Some aspects of Soviet support, however, would not have been necessarily welcome at some levels.

"Listen most carefully O my beauties, O stars of the East, tho' Allah blesseth our Russian ally, anyone found concealing a single copy of Karl Marx will most surely be for the chop."

US nuclear alert

Two days before the end of the 20-day Israeli-Arab War in 1973, US intelligence reported that the USSR was planning to intervene. In response, the US government activated Defense Readiness Condition 3 – a level of preparation for possible imminent conflict. The consequential movement of troops was picked up by Soviet intelligence. The US then stated that the alert was not to prepare for war but to warn the Soviets not to intervene, and the crisis passed.

"Our nuclear alert sure put the clock back in this neck of the woods."

Oil crisis

Following the 1973 Israeli-Arab War, the Organization of the Petroleum Exporting Countries dramatically raised the price of its oil and cut back significantly on its supply to a number of Western countries. The organization stated that its move was 'in response to the US decision to re-supply the Israeli military' during the Yom Kippur War. Before 1973, the world had got used to a plentiful supply of inexpensive fuels – coal, petroleum and natural gas, with national economies dependent not just on these fossil fuels but also on their relatively low cost. The events of 1973 had many repercussions for the UK, including the introduction of a three-day working week, affecting much of the country's industry. Giles illustrated another consequence.

"Left foot, then your right foot, there's a good boy! Beastly Arabs, making our poor Algy walk to school."

Commonwealth Games

The 1974 New Zealand Commonwealth Games were the first major international sporting event held after the 1972 Munich Olympics, where 11 Israeli athletes were killed by terrorists. Unfortunately, these Games also had their problems: David Bedford, the English runner, received severe shin injuries when they were spiked in the 10,000 m race, and Welshman John Davies tripped and brought down a Kenyan on the finishing line in the steeplechase, causing a highly disputed finish.

"I know you came to New Zealand as a hundred metre sprinter, lad..."

Sunday Express, January 27, 1974

Troubles in Cyprus and the Mediterranean

On July 20, 1974, Turkey launched a military invasion by air, land and sea against Cyprus, which resulted in its occupation of the northern portion of the island. In London, the Minister of Defence announced that the Navy was sending two frigates to lift stranded Britons from the beaches of Northern Cyprus. At the same time, there were also anti-British sentiments being expressed at the far eastern end of the Mediterranean. These factors were the cause of the captain's dilemma.

"The trouble is madam, if I alter course to avoid trouble from Cyprus we stand a greater risk of being torpedoed by Egypt"

British football fans

In 1974, one of the worst years in Britain for football hooliganism, Giles made no attempt to hide his disgust at such behavior in our national sport, and a number of his cartoons expressed his feelings on the subject. So-called fans of many British clubs indulged in this type of activity during this period, but this cartoon targeted the worst elements of Manchester United fans, who caused problems even after their team had won easily at home, 5–1, against Charlton.

"A nice hero's welcome from the United Supporters' Club this is!"

Billie Jean King

Billie Jean King, the famous US tennis player, won 12 Grand Slam women's titles amongst many other titles. She became well-known as a fierce and outspoken objector to sexism in sport and in society in general. King became a major force in women's world sport and was a founder member of the Women's Tennis Association and the Women's Sports Foundation. In 1973 she accepted a challenge from from 55-year-old Bobby Riggs, who played the male chauvinist card, to a 'Battle of the Sexes' and she beat him three sets to nill. Her strongly expressed views were not always well received in some places and Giles suggested, here, that, in the mid-1970s, the senior Wimbledon hierarchy was not part of her fan club.

"Has she gone?"

European fish quotas

At this time, British fisherman, copying tactics introduced by their French counterparts in similar situations, blockaded a number of British ports in protest against the importation of cut-price frozen fish, which was damaging their livelihoods. This action has to be seen against the background in which it was taken. During the early 1970s, the British fishing industry received a series of blows from which it has never really recovered. In 1972 Iceland extended its territorial waters to 50 miles (approx. 86 km) from its coastline preventing other nation's trawlers from working in what were traditional fishing waters. The situation deteriorated with a series of net-cutting incidents on British trawlers that fished the area. Royal Navy vessels were sent to act as a deterrent against further harassment of British fishing boats by the Icelanders and this was known as the Second Cod War. The importation of foreign frozen fish greatly exacerbated the British fishing industry's problems. In protest armadas of fishing boats were anchored at the harbour entrances at Immingham, Grimsby and Newcastle, which caused considerable problems for other groups of port users.

"Captain Hornblower does it again – 'No traffic on the East Coast this time of the year, we'll hire a little boat and sail up as far as Grimsby...'"

UK to stay in EEC

In early 1975, the Labour Cabinet was divided on whether or not to remain in the European Community. At a one-day conference on April 26, the party voted 2–1 to leave. A national referendum was held on June 5, at which the electorate was asked to vote with a simple 'yes' or 'no' to 'Do you think the UK should stay in the European Union?'. Over 67 per cent voted to stay in. Rodney's theory, presumably, did not make him many friends amongst our Continental neighbours.

"Oh dear, Rodney is expounding his theory that now we're the United States of Europe all the blighters should learn to speak English."

First commercial Concorde flight

The first scheduled commercial flights by Concorde commenced in January 1976, but the US authorities quickly banned it from landing in America as a result of complaints from the American public regarding noise disturbance and sonic booms. Eventually, on May 24, permission was given for it to land, but only at Dulles Airport at Washington. Giles lived and worked in Suffolk, an area that had suffered excessive noise disturbance from US aircraft for many years.

"Anyone living in this bit of rural England will deeply sympathise with the New Yorkers over Concorde."

US Bicentenary – Queen's visit

The Queen and Prince Phillip visited the US during July 1976 to mark the Bicentenary of American independence from British control. The six-day tour started at Philadelphia, the leading American city when the colonies rejected the rule of King George III, and finished at Boston where she gave a speech from the balcony of the Old State House from which the Bostonians first heard the Declaration of Independence. The royal couple then went on to Montreal, where she officially opened the Olympic Games.

"You weren't supposed to curtsy, Elmer."

Callaghan's visit to Washington.

On March 9, 1977, British Prime Minister James Callaghan flew to Washington on a Concorde aircraft for a series of meeting with the US President. One of the subjects discussed was America's objections to Concorde landing on American soil and, as a result, commercial flights by the aircraft started in May. At the time, Britain was again suffering severe financial constraints, probably explaining Callaghan's apparent reputation for not giving gratuities.

"My brother-in-law in the British Police cabled me: 'Don't expect no gratuities'"

Queen's Jubilee

The Queen's Silver Jubilee, celebrating the 25th anniversary of her accession to the throne, was taken, by the nation, as a good reason for having a huge party. It was estimated that over one million people lined the streets of London to watch the Royal Family on their way to St. Paul's Cathedral at the start of the celebrations and that millions of people across the country celebrated with their own street parties, as illustrated in this cartoon. Giles illustrates a particularly fervent street of Royalists.

"Damn Joneses – he's wearing a WHITE tie!"

Russian satellite crashes

At this time, US and Canadian experts were searching for radioactive debris from a Soviet nuclear-powered spy satellite, which came down over Alaska or northern Canada. Concern was expressed because the satellite was carrying potentially lethal uranium 235 but Britain's National Radiological Protection Board considered any radioactivity would be highly diluted and unlikely to pose a risk. Two American long-range reconnaissance aircraft reported finding nothing after a 10-hour patrol at high level. At the same time, Canadian aircraft were searching, vainly, at a lower level over an area of 77,700 square km (30,000 square miles) where, it was thought, the satellite came down, somewhere in the country's Northern Territories.

"And what has our little man brought home this time?"

First woman to sail single-handed around the world

New Zealander Dame Naomi James was the first woman to sail single-handed around the world. She left Dartmouth, England in September 1977 and arrived back on June 8, 1978, after 272 days at sea. Her voyage was not entirely incident free – she nearly lost her mast on one occasion, almost capsized at one point and was without radio contact for several weeks. Also, sadly a kitten she took for company was lost overboard during the voyage. She was made a Dame in recognition of her exploit.

"Darling, with your odd habit of always pulling the wrong ropes, promise me you'll never sail round a duck pond on your own"

Bjorn Borg fan club

A major phenomenon of tennis during the 1970s was the adulation heaped upon Bjorn Borg by young girls. He became famous at the age of 17 by winning the Italian Open, and went on to win five consecutive Wimbledon men's finals from 1976. This cartoon appeared in the middle of that period. British player John Lloyd, also known as 'Legs' Lloyd and voted the Sexiest Man in Tennis, played at that year's Wimbledon but was eliminated in the first round of the Men's Singles by American Brian Gottfried.

"Never mind whether I'm a Bjorn Borg or Legs Lloyd fan – get out of my seat!"

Reduction of British motor industry

Industrial strife in the UK car industry at this time was becoming widespread. Ford UK moved towards total shut-down as nearly 40,000 workers, about two-thirds of the total workforce, joined a strike against the government's 5 per cent pay increase limit. The day before this cartoon appeared, the newspapers reported that 26,500 workers at Vauxhall looked set to join in this industrial action. Giles suggested here that, often, there is a silver lining for someone.

"We all got a bonus and a whole two hour break to celebrate our glorious ally – the British motor industry!"

First European elections

The European Assembly Elections held on June 7, 1979 were the first to include the UK. In total, the elections were held in nine countries. The elections allowed Europeans from the member countries to elect 410 more MEPs to the European Parliament and were the first international elections in history. It is unlikely that Daddy and the Frenchman would have had much in common when it came to political issues and it is highly possible that this encounter may have ended with a few harsh words.

"Mind you, Daddy's on a sticky wicket having to argue about Euro-Elections in English"

McEnroe's outburst

American, John McEnroe, was one of the most successful and high-profile players in the history of tennis. He had an aggressive and intense playing style that sometimes spilled over into his behaviour both on and off the court. He did not win the Wimbledon Men's Singles title until 1981. The previous year he reached the finals but was not well-received by the crowd. Attempts to curb the more extreme aspects of his attitude were not always met with a thoughtful response, as illustrated here by Giles.

"I heard you telling young McEnroe we'll have none of his tantrums this week – how did he react?"

French ban on English lamb

The French government had imposed a ban on the importation of British lamb but was considering lifting it. It was feared in the UK that, if this happened, British farmers might decide to take advantage of higher prices across the Channel and, therefore, cause a shortage of meat at Christmas time in this country. A further worrying factor was that a strike by New Zealand's slaughter-men was expected to halt all that country's lamb shipments to the UK, thereby exacerbating the problem.

"Personally speaking, I'd prefer 'L'Entree at Maxims' to 'Roast lamb and two veg' on British Rail"

MCC in Australia

It has to be accepted that Australia is a very big place and that parts of New South Wales can be a little undeveloped. However, it is possible that the Australian taxi driver did not do his utmost to help the English cricket team find their way. It did not matter too much, however, as the 1978/79 tour turned out to be extremely successful for the England team with Australia slumping to defeat. England won the first match by 7 wickets and the second with a 166-run victory, winning the series overall 5–1.

"I knew damn well we shouldn't have asked that Aussie taxi driver for the shortest cut to the practice pitch"

Chapter Six
1980–1990

Russian intervention in Afghanistan

On Christmas Day 1979 Soviet forces entered Afghanistan and took control of the capital, Kabul, in what turned out to be a long and bloody conflict, particularly for the Soviet troops. The West deplored this armed intervention and sided with the Afghans. The Colonel's earlier-held opinions refer, no doubt, to his time on the North-West Frontier, which, in his day, formed British India's border with Afghanistan and was the source of many problems for the Raj.

"I see your old treacherous tribal riff-raff, enemies of the British Raj, are now your glorious allies, Colonel."

SAS attack on Iranian Embassy in London

On April 30, 1980, a siege at the Iranian Embassy in Kensington began when six Iranian gunmen took it over and held 19 people hostage. When the gunmen first took over the Embassy, 26 hostages were taken including the British constable on duty at the Embassy main entrance and two visiting BBC personnel there to collect visas. Five of the hostages were released over the next few days due to health reasons. The police attempted to calm down the situation and to make contact with the gunmen and on the third day of the siege the BBC broadcast a statement prepared by the group. On the last day of the siege, however, the gunmen killed an Embassy staff member and threatened to kill a hostage every 30 minutes. This prompted an order to implement a pre-planned rescue operation. The siege ended on May 5 after a highly dramatic storming of the Embassy by 30 SAS commandos. Millions of people watched the rescue of the hostages live on television, and the excitement and daring nature of the raid captured the imagination of the British public.

"Message from H.Q.: 'All S.A.S. men will enter by the back door.'"

USSR and France in secret peace talks

On May 19, 1980, the French President, Giscard D'Estaing, flew to Warsaw to hold talks with the Soviet leader, Brezhnev, at which the situation regarding Afghanistan and peace generally were discussed. The US expressed a great deal of criticism about this initiative in which it was not involved. It is obvious that, for many people, after so many years of the Cold War, with East and the West measuring up to each other, the concept of world peace was something quite unknown and almost alien.

"I suppose this means peace could break out anywhere without us knowing a thing about it."

Reagan and the bomb

Ronald Reagan became President of the United States on November 4, 1980. This cartoon appeared less than a week later, on the following Remembrance Sunday – an event held, of course, to mark the end of past wars. Some people, obviously including Grandma, may have believed that, based upon his persona as an actor in a number of Hollywood war films, Reagan would have taken some decisive action regarding the Cold War at an early stage of his Presidency.

"Reagan's been elected President for nearly a week and he hasn't dropped it yet – that's £1 you owe me."

Mrs Thatcher in Washington

On February 16, a giant panda from London Zoo called Chia Chia was shipped out 'to begin a courtship' with Ling Ling, a female panda at Washington Zoo. At around the same time, Margaret Thatcher flew to the US on a state visit. It is generally accepted that, as world leaders, Margaret Thatcher and Ronald Reagan got on very well together and that they shared similar views on a number of issues. Giles often liked to join up two independent stories in his work, and this is an example.

"No Ursula, Chia-Chia is not going to Washington to be mated with Mrs Thatcher – Mrs Thatcher is going to Washington to be matey with President Reagan!"

Daily Express, February 17, 1981

Journalists in Northern Ireland

Considerable debate was taking place at this time in Britain about 'cheque-book journalism', prompted by concerns regarding payments for information being made by a newspaper to the relatives of a murderer. The discussion centred on the legitimacy of an editor making payments in return for 'exclusive' information. Under the circumstances in which these journalists found themselves, they should probably have taken the cab and discussed it with their boss later.

"Talking of cheque book journalism, do you think the Editor would object to us taking that cab?"

Royal Wedding – Charles and Diana

Around 600,000 people thronged the streets of London to see Prince Charles and Lady Diana Spencer on their wedding day on July 29, 1981. There was a congregation of 3,500 in St Paul's Cathedral for the service and an estimated 750 million people, globally, watched it on television. Celebrations took place all round the country but few could have been quite as colourful as Grandma's outfit made especially for the occasion. This is Grandma as a monachist as opposed to her anarchist persona.

"You'll have to take it off Grandma – Butch doesn't like it!"

Sebastian Coe – records

Sebastian Coe, now Lord Coe, enjoyed great athletic success during the 1980s, winning the 1,500 m Gold Medal at both the 1980 and 1984 Olympic Games and setting eight outdoor and three indoor world records.

On August 28, 1981, he beat his own world record for the mile, a record that was to remain until it was beaten by Britain's runner, Steve Cram, four years later. Lord Coe is now the Chairman of the London Olympics Organising Committee planned for 2012.

"Thanks to our witty 'Here comes Sebastian Coe' he's now serving everybody else first!"

End of Falklands War

The Falklands War, which commenced on April 2, 1982, ended with the Argentinian surrender on June 14. One of the most memorable events of the war was the famous 'yomp', across the islands, undertaken in record time by the Royal Marines and the Parachute Regiment, carrying full equipment. Ray Buckton was the leader of the train drivers union Aslef at the time and had called a strike on the railways. Giles obviously used this situation to show his displeasure with the strike.

"Mr. Buckton says you walked from one end of the Falklands to the other – so what's so bad about walking from Southampton to Glasgow?"

Queen and Philip in San Francisco

The Queen and Prince Philip toured the West Coast of the United States on a state visit from February 26 to March 7, 1983, and visited a number of cities including San Francisco, where it rained most of the time – as picked up by Giles in this cartoon. Reports at the time said that the Royal Party checked into 46 rooms at the St Francis Hotel – most of these rooms were taken by the media. History records that, in fact, Manhattan Island was purchased by Peter Minuit, Director General of the Dutch colony.

"The Brits bought Manhattan for half what you just paid for that flag."

Charles and Diana in Australia

A few days after the Queen and Prince Phillip returned from their visit to America, Charles and Diana travelled to Australia and New Zealand for a six-week official visit. Some observers considered that Diana's doubts about their relationship and Charles' workload and pressure of his public life were unfortunately exacerbated during this state visit. The crowds, whilst warm to Charles, were besotted with Diana. The Princess insisted that their nine-month old baby, Prince William, travelled with them. Giles' obvious pleasure at drawing a range of military and ceremonial uniforms is illustrated in this cartoon.

Hitler's diaries

In April 1983, the German Magazine *Stern* purchased and published what is said were the diaries of Adolf Hitler. Doubts about their authenticity quickly emerged and they were subsequently revealed to be fakes. The German Archives Office had examined them and declared that they were 'grotesque, superficial fakes made on modern paper, using modern ink and full of historical inaccuracies'. Obviously, it was the sort of document that Grandma could well have produced.

"I didn't SAY she wrote them – I only said that she COULD have written them."

US invasion of Grenada

Grenada, in the Caribbean, is a member of the Commonwealth. On October 25, 1983 the US invaded the island following its concern that an airport being built on the island, and using Cuban labour, would support the Soviet-Cuban build-up in that part of the world. The British government stated that it had had no prior notice of the invasion and the UN General Assembly called it a 'flagrant violation of International law'. The conflict ended on December 15, 1983.

"One thing about living on a less exotic isle than Grenada, you're not likely to get troops dropping in on you without notice."

French hijacking British meat lorries

This was the period of the 'Lamb War', when the French government banned the importation of British lamb, an act that Brussels described as being illegal. This conflict developed into an embarrassment for the Common Market and it was reported that France was ready to remove the ban, being anxious to get back to a state of legality as soon as possible. Giles has captured here the typical impression that some British people have on the romantic nature of our neighbours across the Channel.

"First the good news – President Mitterand has apologised for the hijacking of your lorry, then the bad news – we've got it back."

D-Day 40th anniversary

On the 40th anniversary of the D-Day landings on the French coast, many British and other ex-soldiers who had taken part in the invasion re-visited the beaches. This invasion was the first step towards the liberation of occupied Europe. This is probably one bet that the ex-soldier would have preferred to have lost, and it is certain that Giles, who saw a lot of action when he was with the British forces as a War Correspondent Cartoonist, as they crossed Northern Europe into Germany, would have agreed.

"There it is – June 6, 1944. You bet me £5 this was the war to end all wars. I bet you it wasn't. You owe me £5."

Soviet in space and Olympic Games

The US Olympic authorities were concerned about a possible drugs scandal at the 1984 Los Angeles Games, which opened on July 28. In the spring of that year, some of their athletes had proved positive in an informal drugs test. On July 25, Russian cosmonaut Svetlana Savitskaya became the first woman to carry out a spacewalk while she was on the *Salyut 7* space station. Only three months later, Kathryn Sullivan became the first US woman astronaut to step into space.

"I took an overdose of pep pills for the high jump."

Operation Lionheart in Germany

Operation Lionheart was an important military exercise carried out in West Germany and was the largest deployment of British troops since the Second World War. In addition to British personnel already there, a further 35,000 were transported by air to take part in the exercise, which was designed to test Britain's mobilization procedures and culminated in a major field training exercise. The German frau had, no doubt, vivid memories of the last time British troops stormed across her garden.

"I think what Frau Meyerburger is trying to tell you is that she had only just got her garden tidy since the Second World War."

Miners strike

The Miners' Strike of 1984–5 was a major industrial action that seriously affected British industry. After some sporadic strike activity, the NUM (the miners' union) declared a National Strike, which started on May 12, 1984.

The situation became very acrimonious and many meetings between the combatants were held to discuss the miners' grievances, but to no avail – as alluded to in this cartoon. Almost a year after its start, on March 3, 1985, the strike was ended without any new agreements being reached.

"In that case what's the point in having talks?"

Cold War – exchanging spies

On September 23, 1985, on information provided by Oleg Gordievsky, a former head of the Russian KGB who defected to Britain, the government expelled 25 Soviet embassy staff, named by Gordievsky as spies, including journalists and diplomats. In response, three days later the Russians expelled 25 Britons from the British Embassy in Moscow. This state of affairs caused considerable debate in Parliament and, no doubt, lots of headaches for those trying to organize the swap-over.

"Mr Gorbachev? I've lost count – is it us to you or you to us today?"

Charles and Diana in Australia

During this trip to Australia, Charles expressed anger that his 'off the cuff' remarks about inner-city violence in England had appeared in some newspapers and complained that he had been misquoted. Around this time, Diana commented that she preferred her full name to be used rather than 'Di'. Probably the lady here was concerned that her husband, all dressed up in his Sunday clothes might, inadvertently, contribute to the rather sensitive atmosphere prevailing at the time.

"When you shake hands remember she doesn't like being called 'Di' and she certainly won't like being called 'Sheila'."

Decision to build Channel Tunnel

Earlier, in November 1984, the British and French governments decided to resume the project for a Channel crossing and, in April 1985, possible promoters were invited to submit schemes. A number of schemes were submitted involving both bridges and tunnels. On January 20, 1986, the tunnel scheme, prepared by a consortium of British and French design and construction companies, was accepted. It is doubtful that the English businessman agreed totally with his French friend.

"It'll be much more fun knowing your wife could hop over in three hours."

Branson and Blue Riband race across the Atlantic

Sir Richard Branson crossed the Atlantic, from the US to Britain, in record time, in his powerboat *Virgin Atlantic Challenger II*. He completed the 4,800 km (3,000-mile) voyage in 3 days, 8 hours and 31 minutes, and recaptured the Blue Riband for the UK, which had been held since 1952 by the liner SS *United States* for a crossing of 3 days and 10 hours. The Blue Riband is an informal challenge for the fastest sea crossing across the Atlantic and was established in 1838 by the main shipping companies.

"He holds that none of them have beaten the Cutty Sark yet, under sail."

Commonwealth Games in Edinburgh

The Edinburgh Commonwealth Games, held in July 1986, were marred by a significant political boycott. A large number of African, Asian and Caribbean nations stayed away in protest at Britain continuing to undertake sporting activities with South Africa, which still had an apartheid regime. Of the 59 countries of the Commonwealth, only 26 participated, causing a depleted event that also created severe financial problems for the organizers and, in particular, the city of Edinburgh.

"If many more of them back out, bang goes my new Rover."

Big Bang in the City

On October 27, 1986, the Stock Market was deregulated, which brought in sweeping changes in the operation of the London Stock Exchange. These included the abolition of fixed commission charges, which completely altered the market's structure, and the replacement of 'open outcry' trading with business being undertaken on computer screens and telephones. Some people consider that this so-called 'Big Bang' contributed to the financial world's problems that surfaced in 2008.

"It would take more than a big bang in the City to wake our Florrie."

French PM calls Mrs Thatcher a housewife

At a Common Market meeting, the French Prime Minister, Mitterrand, accused Mrs Thatcher of bringing 'housewife' economics into the debate. This was in response to a fiery outburst from the British prime minister in which she said that the Community was facing bankruptcy and that, 'You cannot spend money you have not got'. In 1989, British newspapers reported that, following another acrimonious meeting, Chirac said of her – 'What does she want, this housewife? My balls on a tray!'

"Mrs Thatcher didn't like being called only a housewife. Nor did my wife."

Comic Relief

Started in 1985, Comic Relief was intended to inspire the nation to 'have a laugh' while at the same time raising money to help the poor, the vulnerable and the disadvantaged, both at home and abroad. The 1988 event brought in over £15 million. The Red Nose Day initiative, now a core activity of the whole exercise, commenced during the 1988 event and it is likely that this cartoon by Giles contributed greatly to the success of the new project by giving it such a high level of publicity.

"You asked for that – 'Funny comic nose, Madam? Oh, I see you've already got one?'"

Eddie the Eagle

At Calgary in 1988, Eddie 'the Eagle' Edwards was the first ever British competitor in the Winter Olympics Ski Jumping event. He was not well equipped for the event and, some felt, had inadequate training. He finished 58th out of 58 competitors, as the 59th competitor broke a leg. Despite this, he became the event's hero and received more requests for interviews from the media than any other entrant. In 1990, the rules for entering the Games were changed and Eddie could no longer participate.

"Bravo! You've beaten Eddie Edwards' record 58th place out of 58 – you're 59th."

Daily Express, February 18, 1988

Russians leaving Afghanistan

Soviet forces entered Afghanistan in December 1979 to help prop-up its struggling communist government. This had caused great concern to the US and Afghanistan's neighbours. After nine years of a costly and bloody occupation, an agreement was reached for the Soviets to withdraw their forces, gradually, over a period of nine months. Critics of the move, however, feared that, after the Soviet troops left, the country would slip into anarchy and, in fact, civil war continued following their departure.

"My grandfather can remember when the Bengal Lancers used the Afghans for rifle practice for well over a century."

Poll tax

The introduction of the Poll Tax caused more public anger and resentment than almost any other government initiative in the period since the Second World War. The unrest generated a large number of demonstrations and meetings throughout the country, with many people refusing to pay the tax. In consequence, local authorities, the bodies charged with collecting the tax, were obliged to go to great lengths to get the money in and to track down the non-payers wherever they were.

"Private Wilkinson? For you – final demand for Poll Tax from Islington Borough Council."

Channel Tunnel – meeting of drilling teams

Construction on the Channel Tunnel started in September 1987, with boring teams working from both the French and British sides. The chosen scheme comprised three tunnels and was one of the biggest civil engineering projects of the 20th century. The scheme provided a central service tunnel, with train tunnels on either side. The service tunnel was the first to link up in November 1990 and the whole project finally opened for passenger use on November 14, 1994.

"Butch has slipped his lead and gone off to Paris for lunch."

Index

Acknowledgements

Executive Editor: Trevor Davies

Editor: Ruth Wiseall

Creative Director: Tracy Killick

Deputy Creative Director: Karen Sawyer

Designer: Sally Bond

Production Controller: Linda Parry

More great titles from Hamlyn

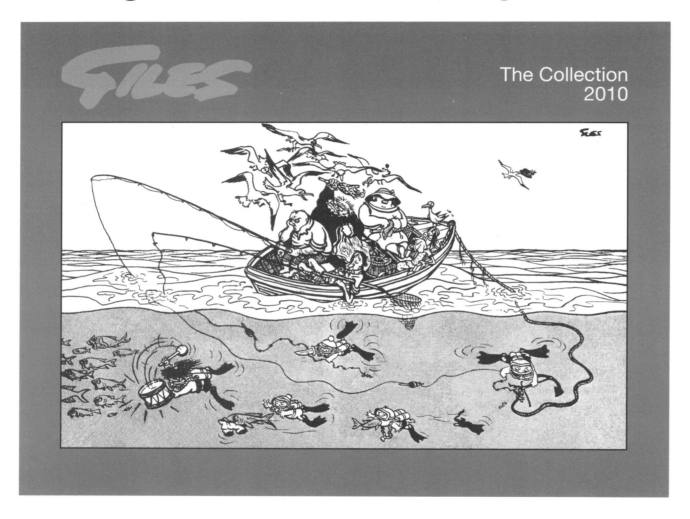

Giles: The Collection 2010
978-0-600-62046-4
£7.99

Celebrate the reputable wit and artistry of Carl Giles with this brand new collection of his best-loved cartoons from the archives of the Daily Express and Sunday Express. Sure to have you reminiscing and laughing for hours, this compilation is a must for every Giles fan.